Bla

A Play

Davey Anderson

A SAMUEL FRENCH ACTING EDITION

FOUNDED 1830

SAMUELFRENCH.COM
SAMUELFRENCH-LONDON.CO.UK

FOR PRODUCTION ENQUIRIES

UNITED STATES AND CANADA
Info@SamuelFrench.com
1-866-598-8449

UNITED KINGDOM AND EUROPE
Plays@SamuelFrench-London.co.uk
020-7255-4302/01

Each title is subject to availability from Samuel French, depending upon country of performance. Please be aware that *BLACKOUT* may not be licensed by Samuel French in your territory. Professional and amateur producers should contact the nearest Samuel French office or licensing partner to verify availability.

MUSIC USE NOTE

Licensees are solely responsible for obtaining formal written permission from copyright owners to use copyrighted music in the performance of this play and are strongly cautioned to do so. If no such permission is obtained by the licensee, then the licensee must use only original music that the licensee owns and controls. Licensees are solely responsible and liable for all music clearances and shall indemnify the copyright owners of the play(s) and their licensing agent, Samuel French, against any costs, expenses, losses and liabilities arising from the use of music by licensees. Please contact the appropriate music licensing authority in your territory for the rights to any incidental music.

IMPORTANT BILLING AND CREDIT REQUIREMENTS

If you have obtained performance rights to this title, please refer to your licensing agreement for important billing and credit requirements.

BLACKOUT

Blackout was commissioned by the National Theatre and premiered as part of their Theatre of Debate season at the Lyttelton Theatre on 4th July 2008.

The play was developed with the support of the Citizens Theatre / TAG Theatre Company and was first performed by members of the Citizens Young Co:

Fraser Hamilton
James Harkness
Rea Karnowski
Katrina Lamont
Martin McLeod

Director Davey Anderson
Young Co. Director Neil Packham
Assistant Director Rea Karnowsli

This production was then revived by the Citizens Theatre / TAG Theatre Company and toured schools throughout Glasgow with the following cast:

Claire Dyer
Fraser Hamilton
James Harkness
Keira Lucchesi
Scott McKay

The play was subsequently performed by various young theatre companies across the UK as part of the New Connections programme 2009. It has also been translated into Portuguese and performed by teenagers in São Paulo, Brazil as part of Conexões 2009.

AUTHOR'S NOTE

I wrote this play, but the story isn't mine. It belongs to a young man from the east end of Glasgow who allowed me to interview him about his life. He was eighteen at the time and was being mentored because, when he was fifteen, he committed a violent crime and was currently serving a probation sentence.

We met in a small room with sofas and we talked. Sometimes we drank tea. I asked questions and he answered. I was amazed by how articulate he was and how willing to share his thoughts, feelings and anecdotes. I went away with several hours of audio recordings from our conversations, which I then edited into a short narrative.

This is not to say that the following text is a verbatim transcript — although most of the words are his rather than mine. The play that emerged is a fictionalised account of the events surrounding the crime this young man committed, told with a fair amount of creative licence and, crucially, with certain key details left out.

The play was written to be performed by members of the Citizens Young Co, based at the Citizens Theatre in the Gorbals, Glasgow. It was written before I knew whether I would be working with only one or, potentially, twenty performers. It is therefore flexible in terms of cast size and works best, I think, when the performers form a tight, physically energetic ensemble.

In the original production there were no lights, no sound effects, no music, no specific costumes and the set consisted of four chairs with the audience seated on three sides surrounding the stage. Of course, other productions have been and will be more elaborate than this. My only request to directors is that you leave some things to the audience's imagination.

Davey Anderson

CHARACTERS

James
Ma
Da
Grandda
Polis Guy
Key Worker
Teacher
Friends
Bullies
Friends of Friends
Judge

All the members of the performing company act as a chorus, or a collective of storytellers

For James (both of them)

ACKNOWLEDGEMENTS

This play could not have been written without the support of Barnardo's Youth Involvement Project, Easterhouse. Special thanks to Oli Higham and Frank Connelly.

BLACKOUT

ONE

Imagine
You wake up
You open your eyes
And you're like that
Where am I?
A small room
Bright lights
White walls
A metal door
Oh my God!
Imagine you wake up and you're in a jail cell.
You go up to the door
You bang your fists
Screaming
Shouting
What am I doing in here?
And imagine the polis guy comes up to the door
And he's like that
Keep it doon.
And you're like
Whit did I dae?
Aw, you don't know?
You shake your head
Whit?
And the polis guy just looks at you like you're a pure thug or something.
Imagine he just looks at you and he goes

You're getting charged with attempted murder, wee man.
You'd be like that
Aw naw
What did I do?
And you'd start remembering
Everything
Right from the beginning
You would try to remember
How did I get here?

Two

So you'd start remembering your dad.
He was a woman beater.
He beat up your mum every day
From the day they got married right up to the day they got divorced
He used to beat her to a pulp.
So she stopped working
She wouldn't go out the house
Cos she was embarrassed.
She didn't want to walk down the street with her face all black and
    blue.
And you'd remember that your ma didnae want you to grow up to be
    like him.
She wanted you to be a famous lawyer
Or a famous doctor
Or a famous whatever.
And you'd remember that you were poor.
But you weren't poor poor
Cos your mum still made sure there was a dinner on the table every
    night.
She'd give you her last penny
She didn't care about herself.
But you'd remember that you never really spoke to her.
Cos you'd come home from school and go straight up the stairs.

James?
Aye.
Your dinner's out.
You'd come down
Grab the plate
Thanks, Ma.
Back up the stairs.
So you never really spoke to her.

THREE

But you'd remember your granddad.
He was the closest thing you had to a proper father.
He put you under his wing
He did everything a dad would do
He'd hold your hand
He'd walk you down to the shops
He'd play daft wee games with you
But best of all, he'd take you to the Rangers game every Saturday.
He'd take you to see the Orange Walks.
You'd remember how he taught you to play the flute
But you'd not to play The Sash
Or hang the Ulster flag out the window.
He taught you to keep that kind of thing to yourself.
But then he got his cancer.
You'd remember that.
So every night you'd go and sit with him
Play a game of cards
Help him do a jigsaw
Have a cup of tea and look out the back window.
You'd remember that that was where the boys fae your scheme used to
    fight with the boys fae the scheme doon the road.
They'd run at each other with bottles and bricks
Then it would be poles and baseball bats
And then it would be knives.

You'd be looking out the window going
Is that a wee boy with a sword?
Am I really seeing this?
And you and your granddad
You would just sit there and go
What are they fighting for?
Cos your grandda never went out and started hitting people.
He got his point across with his mouth, not with his hands.
He would just have to talk to you and people would listen to him.
And you'd remember you always wanted to grow up to be just like
    him.

FOUR

But when you were growing up, you didnae have that many pals.
Cos you were too quiet
You were shy
You were the wee, shy, nerdy boy
You didnae fit in with anybody.
And the pals you did have, they just used you, if you know what I
    mean.
Cos, know if it was a pure brilliant sunny day, they would all go away
    and leave you in the house.
But know if it was raining outside, they would come roon tae your bit
    and go
Hi James
I've no seen you in ages
How have you been?
Can we come in and sit for a while?
They didnae care about you
They just wanted somewhere tae sit.

FIVE

And say it was at school
You would get beaten up for being a goth

Just cos you had long hair and wore black combats.
They used to call you
The gimp!
Haw, look at him.
Ya dirty goth!
Dae you shag deid people?
Whit?
You go up the graveyards and hing aboot there, din't ye?
Naw.
Aye ye dae. I've seen ye.
Pure digging up the coffins and raping the corpses.
Ya dirty beast!
And you'd remember the beatings.
One of the bullies would take off his belt
He'd wrap it round his knuckles
And whack you with it.
Ah!!!
Then they'd throw you down the stairs
Don't!
Kick you in the ribs
Stop it!
Death to the gimp!!
And they would swagger off
And leave you there, lying on the ground
Curled up into a wee ball.
You'd remember that.
You'd remember every punch.

Six

And you'd remember you had nobody to turn to
Cos your grandda was in the hospital
So you'd just sit in your room and watch horror films
Night after night
Or read books about serial killers.

Or just look at all the pictures.
You had a bloodlust for it.
It gave you a thrill
Reading about killers
Cos they're normal people
But they're mysterious.
What makes them tick?
What makes them go insane?
What can make somebody dae it tae somebody?
It fascinated you.

SEVEN

Imagine
You're in a jail cell
And you start remembering all this.
But you can't remember what you've done.
And then they take you to a Secure Care Unit
And they take away your belt
And they take away your laces
And they take away anything you could use to try and kill yourself.
Then this key worker guy comes in to speak to you
And you ask him
What did I do?
Son, I can't tell you.
How can you no tell me?
You need to ask for a file.
So you ask for the file
And he goes away to get it.
Imagine waiting for him to come back.
Your mind would be racing
Remembering …

EIGHT

Wan night
You got beaten up, just for having long hair.
These boys chased you home with meat cleavers and machettes
Shouting
Death to the gimp!
Trying to chop you up
All the way to your front door.
Hi James.
How was school?
Straight up the stairs
Into your bedroom
Slam!
You look in the mirror.
I'm not a gimp.
You get a pair of scissors
You cut your hair pure short
Shave it right to the skin.
James?
Then you look at yourself.
Your dinner's out.
I'm coming.
I'll show them no tae mess about wae me.
Grab the plate.
Thanks, Ma.
Wait a wee minute.
What?
What happened to your hair?
You shrug.
I got rid of it.
She looks at you funny.
You look like a skinhead.

NINE

That's when you started watching films like Romper Stomper
And American History X
And you thought to yourself
That's whit I'll dae.
So you started wearing the big Doc Marten boots
The bomber jacket
The braces
Everything.

TEN

And then you went into school.
And people would just look at you like
Ooff
He's a pure psycho.
But it felt good
Cos you were getting tae them.
And then you'd dae the Nazi salute
And the teachers were like
Stand outside this room.
What have you got this on for?
Cos I like it.
Go home and change into your uniform.
You're not allowed back into the school until you change your
    clothes.
So you went
Fine. It's my life. I'll wear what I want. I'll say what I want. I'll dae
    what I want.
And you sparked up a fag
And started walking about the school
Smoking
Acting like a hard man.
Haw, look

Check the state of him.
And when the bullies saw you, instead of running away, you went
Right, who's first?
Whit you gonnae dae, ya daftie?
Two seconds.
Whit?
And you went
fssssssssssssss
You put the fag out on your bare skin.
Who's first then?
Are you awright?
C'mon, who's gieing me the first punch?
James…
Go. I'll put my hands behind my back.
You need tae get your heid sorted oot, mate. You're no right.
Then you pick up a chair
And throw it at the fucker.
So he starts punching you
Fists flying
They all start battering you.
James!!
What are you doing?
That's not like you.
But you're standing there
With your face red raw.
Aw, it feels great but, din't it?

Eleven

And you'd remember that that's when you started loving the pain.
The punches didnae hurt anymore.
You just got used to having that energy flow
That feeling of blood pumping through your veins.
And you'd sit there in your room
With the big Nazi posters up on the wall

And you'd listen to music
With that guitar
And that beat that gets you intae it
And you'd wonder what it was like to burst somebody's lip
Or to slice them open
To butcher them.
It made you feel high and mighty just thinking about it.

TWELVE

And you'd remember the night that it finally happened …
It was raining.
James?
That's your mum
Shouting up the stairs.
You turn off the music.
I'm just away up the hospital to see your granddad.
You don't respond.
D'you want to come with me?
No the night, ma.
Are ye sure?
Nah, I want to stay in and watch this film.
Well, d'you want to go up and see him the morra night?
Aye, Ma. Fine.
Right.
I'll tell him you were asking after him.
See you later.
She goes out into the rain.
You put on a slasher film.
Slash
Chop
Rip
Stab
Blood and guts.
You look at it blankly.

It's not enough for you anymore.
Then there's a knock at the door.
You press pause
Open the door.
Awright, James.
Awright.
Whit ye daeing?
Nothing. Just sitting in my room.
Is yer maw in?
Naw.
Are you on your own?
Aye.
Yas, man, big Jim's got an empty!
Yas!
They all crowd in.
C'mon.
D'ye want a joint?
Emmm, no the noo.
Whit ye watching?
Nothing.
What's this?
That's a Swastika.
Whit ye daeing with a Swastika on your wall?
Are you a Nazi or something?
Snigger
Aye.
They all look at you.
Whit ye intae all that for?
Cos. I'm an Arian. I need tae protect my white blood.
Oh aye. And how are ye gonnae dae that?
Wait till you see this.
You slip your hand under the bed
And you pull out a sword.
Fuck's sake.
What is that?
A Black Mamba.

Where d'ye get it?
I found it.
Did ye fuck?
How much did that set ye back?
You shrug.
I'll buy it aff ye for a fiver.
Nut.
A tenner then.
Fuck off.
Twenty quid.
Check the damage ye could dae wae that.
Have ye chopped somebody yet?
You smile
So proud.
Look at him
The psycho.
Then …
Keys in the door.
Quick
Hide the blade.
Footsteps on the stairs.
What's going on here?
Nothing, Mum.
Suspicious.
You only call her "Mum" when you've done something wrong.
We're just watching a film.
I think it's time your friends went home.
See ye after.
Bye James.
Catch ye.
They disappear
And your mum just looks at you.
James, sit down, I've got something to tell you.
Don't, Ma.
I'm sorry, James.
Ma, don't!

James, calm down.
Don't.
I'm sorry. It happened.

THIRTEEN

That's what you'd remember
You'd remember the night that your grandda died.
That's when you died inside.
You'd remember how you wanted to hold somebody down to the
   ground
And stab their eyes out.
Or get a baseball bat
And skelp it aff somebody's heid
Just to get the anger out of you
Cos it was building up
All this anger
And you didnae have a way to let it out.

FOURTEEN

Imagine that all this is going through your head as you're waiting in a
   wee room with no belt and no laces.
And then the key worker guy comes back with your file.
He hands it to you and you start to read
But you can't concentrate on the words
So you ask him to read it for you.
What does it say?
Gonnae just tell tell me!
Do you really not remember?
You shake your head.
Assault.
Arson.
Attempted murder.

Do you remember now?
Some of it.
Why don't you tell me what happened?
I'll try.
So you start to tell the story…

FIFTEEN

Where were you?
You were in the town.
Who were you with?
You were with your pals.
Your pals' pals.
People they knew.
But you didn't know them?
Naw.
Where were your friends?
They all went away and left you with these folk you didnae know.
Why?
You don't know.
But it starts coming back to you.
One of them hands you a bottle of vodka.
Here, d'you want a stank?
And you're like
Aye.
Drink it straight.
How?
Just drink it straight.
So you went
You took a wee bit of it.
It tasted weird.
Naw, here
Something's wrang wae this.
And they went
Just down it.

And you went
Fine.
Cos you didnae want tae look like the wee nerdy boy.
And you took a big stank of it.
And there was ecstasy
And there was vallium
And you didnae know what was in it.
And by the time your pals came back, you were in some state.
James?
You were like Doctor Jekyll and Mr Hyde.
Awright, mate?
Cos wan minute you'd be fine.
Where have ye been? I've been pure missing ye.
And then the next minute
Aye, where have ye been, aye, where have ye been, aye, where have
    ye been?
Like that
Leaving me here, aye? D'ye want me to come over there and smash
    ye aboot?
Calm doon.
And you were looking at people.
But you werenae just looking at them.
You were looking at them like you were picking a victim.
James, come on
We need to get you hame.
And you remember them taking you hame.
But then…

SIXTEEN

All you can remember is
Screaming
You could hear screaming.
It was like being in a dream
But still being awake at the same time.

And all you can hear is
James?
Are you all right?
And you can feel your blood boiling over.
What's happened to you?
What have you took?
James?
And you start punching
James, don't!
And kicking
James, stop it!
And you feel your hands around somebody's throat.
What are you doing?
Squeezing.
Don't!
Stop it!
Please!
James!
Don't!
And then screaming
And then
Everything went black.

SEVENTEEN

Imagine you did that to somebody.
And you don't know why you did it.
You just
You wanted payback.
You were hurting so much
You wanted to hurt somebody else.
But the payback you done, you didnae mean.
You just needed a friend.
You just needed someone to talk to.
But instead you nearly killed somebody that night.

Aye
You remember
You remember it all.

EIGHTEEN

Now imagine this
They take you to a court room
And they put you in front of a judge
And the judge says
Son, I see thousands of boys like you
Every year
Getting charged with these exact same crimes.
And most of them end up in jail for anything up to ten years.
And you're standing there
Shaking like a leaf
Thinking
God.
Ten years.
Please don't.
That's me finished.
Then she says
But some of them
I look at some of them standing there
And I know they don't belong in jail.
I know they just made a stupid mistake
And what they really need is somebody to give them a chance.
And she looks you right in the eye.
You're one of the lucky ones.
I'm going to give you a probation sentence.
Three years.
And you're like
Thank you.
But if you mess up during that time, you'll do ten years in jail.
Do you understand?

Yes.
You may leave my courtroom.
That's you free to go.

NINETTEN

You step outside
Into the sunshine
You take a deep breath
And there's your mum
Waiting.
She looks at you.
You look at her.
How is she ever gonnae trust you again?
But she walks towards you
Mum, I'm sorry.
And she bursts out greeting.
Then she goes
What are you going to do with yourself?

TWENTY

Imagine.
Imagine if all that happened to you.
What would you do?
You know what I would do?
I would start to talk.
I would tell people my story.
Cos when I got angry
I nearly lost everything.
And all I really wanted was somebody to sit up and take notice.
And then you would go home
You would take down all your Nazi posters
You'd get rid of all your knifes

You would look in the mirror and try to imagine
What comes next?
And then you'd get into bed
You'd pull up the covers
And you'd turn off the light.
Blackout.

Lightning Source UK Ltd.
Milton Keynes UK
UKOW06f1108210415

250014UK00015B/512/P